FOLLOW ME

JoAnne Nelson
Pictures by Mark Anthony

MODERN CURRICULUM PRESS

DEVELOPMENTAL EDITOR: Diane Arnell
PROJECT EDITOR: Judith E. Nayer
DESIGN & PRODUCTION: Thomasina Webb
ART DIRECTION: Bob Feldgus
MEDIA EDITOR: Glenn E. Conner
MUSIC COMPOSITION/PRODUCTION: Michael Lobel

Published by Modern Curriculum Press

Modern Curriculum Press, Inc.
A division of Simon & Schuster
13900 Prospect Road, Cleveland, Ohio 44136

This edition is published simultaneously in Canada
by Globe/Modern Curriculum Press, Toronto.

Manufactured in the United States of America

ISBN 0-8136-3760-0 (STY PK)   ISBN 0-8136-3756-2 (BK)
10   9   8   7   6   5   4   92   91   90

I went for a walk
and what did I see?

A little red puppy
was following me.

I went for a walk
and what did I see?

A fluffy orange kitten
was following me.

I went for a walk
and what did I see?

A pretty blue bird
was following me.

I went for a walk
and what did I see?

A jumping green frog
was following me.

I went for a walk
and what did I see?

A soft yellow duckling
was following me.

I went for a walk
and what did I see?

14

A round purple bug
was following me.

When I got home, what did I see?
They all came in
and had lunch with me.